I AM enough

SELF CARE BIBLE STUDY & COLORING PRAYER JOURNAL

A 5 Week Guided Bible Study for Women, Scripture Writing
Notebook Prayer Journal with Prompts & Coloring Pages
for Creative Bible Journaling

JoDitt Williams

I am Enough: Self-Care Bible Study & Coloring Prayer Journal
A 5 Week Guided Bible Study for Women, Scripture Writing Notebook Prayer Journal with Prompts & Coloring Pages for Creative Bible Journaling

JoDitt Designs
Stephenville, TX 76401
joditt.com | facebook.com/jodittw | instagram.com/jodittw | pinterest.com/joditt

This journal
belongs to:

_____

Free I Am Enough Bonus Kit

To help you get the most from this book I created some additional resources for you, including:

- **Virtual Workshop:** How to Connect with Jesus thru Asking Questions
- Printable & digital coloring pages
- Lockscreens/Wallpapers for your phone
- Printable/digital word art
- Printable/digital stickers

Get the Free Kit at:
shop.joditt.com/iaebook-bonus

Let's Connect!

Join my **Delight in the Word with JoDitt Facebook group** at **facebook.com/groups/DelightInTheWord/** to connect with other women who are going through this study, get daily inspiration and encouragement, and to learn about upcoming live events.

Learn more about delighting in the Word of God using color and creativity by visiting my blog at: **joditt.com**

Contents

Why Study Self Care?

Have you ever noticed that you are more easily irritated and/or discouraged when you are tired and/or hurting, either physically or emotionally?

Well, the devil has sure noticed and he loves to take advantage of us when we are at our weakest. That is one reason why it is so important to take care of yourself and to prioritize self-care.

In these modern times, we wear busy-ness like a badge of honor, and brag about how little sleep we run on.

- Rest is considered as being lazy.
- Down-time is thought of as a luxury.
- And taking time to smell the roses seems impossible...
  ...when we already feel like we always need more hours in the day to get everything done that needs done.

The problem is...
... even though we are constantly BUSY, we are not actually being very productive, and we are running ourselves down, both physically and emotionally.

However, God sets a very different example for us. This study is designed to help you discover God's perspective of self-care, and to help to answer the following questions:
- Why is self-care important
- How to practice self-care without feeling guilty
- How to find the time, without neglecting others
- When is self-care selfish

This book is also designed to help you practice self-care in the process of studying it, by included coloring along with the Bible study... because coloring has been proven to reduce stress and help with relaxation. Coloring is so easy that anyone can do it, and it is so fun and rewarding to create something beautiful by adding colors that make your heart smile.

How to Use this Journal

The **Bible Reading Plan** is divided up into 5 weeks with 6 days per week. There 2 journal pages per day, with an blank page at the end of each week. Use the blank page to write a summary of what you learned for the week, or to doodle/illustrate/hand-letter your biggest take-away, or just to test the colors of your colored pencils or markers.

Begin your study time by coloring in the header. This simple act will help you to switch on the right side of your brain, which will make it easier for you to connect with the heart of God.

Each day, read the Bible verses listed in the header. I recommend looking up the verses in several different Bible translations. This is very easy to do using an app like the You Version Bible app.

Use the lined journal area on the left page to write out one or more of the verses from that day's reading. Then record your observations in the box below. Writing out Scripture requires you to slow down and pay more attention. You will find that you notice things when writing the verses, that you did not notice when reading or listening to the verse. I left a wide margin on each left-hand page so that you can write/doodle/draw/trace/color, etc.

ASK JESUS: Each day includes a question for you to ask Jesus. Picture Jesus sitting there with you. See how delighted He is to be with you. Ask him the suggested question and write whatever comes to you in the box. Then write your response to Jesus' answer in the My Response box.
(Get my FREE Virtual Workshop about this at: **shop.joditt.com/iaebook-bonus**)

At the end of the journal are some bonus pages:
· **Clipart & Word Art** - Copy this page, then trace onto the margins of this journal or onto the margins of your journaling Bible. Or copy onto cardstock, then color, cut and glue onto journal cards to create your own Scripture memory cards.
· **Bookmarks/Bible Journaling Templates** - Cut out & color to use as bookmarks, or use them as templates to trace into the margins of this journal, or in your journaling Bible.
· **Coloring Pages** - Enjoy meditating on the Word of God while coloring them. Then cut out, frame and display in your home or office as beautiful reminders.

Self Care
Bible Reading Plan

Why Take Care of You

- Genesis 1:27, 31
- Ephesians 2:10
- Ephesians 1:4-6
- 1 Peter 5:6-7
- 3 John 1:2
- Mark 12:31

What Did Jesus Do

- Genesis 2:2-3
- Mark 1:35
- Luke 5:16*
- Mark 6:31-32
- Matthew 6:25-26
- Luke 10:38-42

Caring for Your Body

- Psalm 139:13-16
- 1 Corinthians 6:19-20
- 1 Timothy 4:7-8
- Proverbs 31:17
- 1 Corinthians 10:31
- Romans 12:1

Caring for Your Mind

- 2 Timothy 1:7
- Philippians 4:8
- Romans 12:2
- Psalm 119:15
- Colossians 3:2
- 1 Peter 1:13

Caring for Your Heart

- Psalm 23: 1-3
- Matthew 11:28-29
- Isaiah 53:4-5
- Psalm 1:1-3
- Philippians 4:11-13
- Psalm 34:1-5

CHAPTER 1

Why Take Care of You

If you struggle with making time to take care of yourself because you are too busy taking care of everybody else, it may be because you do not realize your own worth. Therefore, this study on self-care begins by finding out how God sees you and what he thinks about you. This chapter will also help you discover what reasons the Bible gives for taking care of yourself.

Genesis 1:27, 31

God created mankind
in his own image

Observations

Whose image were you created in?

_____

Who created you?

_____

What did God think about everything he had made?

_____

_____

If you have children that look, sound or act like you, how
does that make you feel?

_____

_____

_____

_____

_____

_____

_____

_____

_____

_____

_____

_____

_____

_____

_____

_____

_____

Ask Jesus

How do I look, sound, think or act like God?

My Response

Ephesians 2:10

Observations

What does this verse say we are?

_____

How were we created?
_____

Why were we created?
_____

_____

Have you ever made anything good?
_____

If so, how did that make you feel?
_____

How would you feel if someone did not take good care

of something you made?
_____

_____

How do you feel when other people do not take good

care of themselves?
_____

_____

_____

_____

_____

_____

_____

_____

Ask Jesus

How does it make you feel when I
don't take care of myself?

My Response

Ephesians 1:4-6

Observations

Who does verse 4 say chose us?

_____

_____

When were we chosen?

_____

_____

Why were we chosen?

_____

_____

_____

What are we chosen for?

_____

_____

_____

How were we chosen?

_____

_____

_____

How did God feel about choosing us?

_____

_____

_____

_____

_____

_____

_____

_____

_____

_____

Ask Jesus

Why did you choose me?

My Response

Chapter 1
Day 4

*See coloring bookmark/
template on page 91

1 Peter 5:6-7

Observations

What 2 things do these verses instruct us to do?

Is it humbling to you to admit that you cannot fix
everything for everyone?

Why or why not?

What will God do after we humble ourselves?

What reason does this verse give as to why we can cast
our cares on Jesus?

If Jesus is our example, and he cares for you, do you
think it is OK for you to care for you?

Why or why not?

Ask Jesus

What worries, cares & anxieties do I need to
cast on you today?

My Response

3 John 1:2

_____

_____

_____

_____

_____

_____

_____

_____

_____

_____

_____

_____

Observations

According to this verse...

What must prosper before we can prosper in all things
and be in health?

_____

What is the meaning of the word "prosper" in this verse?

_____

_____

_____

_____

Does God want your soul to prosper?

Does God want you to be in health?

Does God want you to prosper in all things?

_____

_____

In what ways are you cooperating with God to make
sure your health and soul are prospering?

_____

_____

In what ways are you neglecting the health of your body,
mind and soul?

_____

_____

_____

_____

Ask Jesus

Is my soul prospering?
Why or why not?

My Response

*See coloring page on page 21

Mark 12:31

Observations

How does Jesus say we are to love our neighbor?

_____

_____

Does Jesus say we should love our neighbor more than we

love ourself?

_____

Do you think it is possible to truly love your neighbor if

you don't love yourself?

_____

_____

How well do you love yourself? (On a scale of 1-10)

_____

_____

What are some specific ways you choose to love

yourself today / this week / this year?

_____

_____

_____

_____

_____

What things are you doing for others in the name of

love, that are actually just you trying to control or

manipulate, or get sympathy or approval, or to punish

yourself because you feel guilty?

_____

_____

_____

_____

Ask Jesus

What is blocking me from
loving myself like you love me?

My Response

Love others as well as you love yourself

mark 12 : 31

JoDitt
© joditt.com

21

CHAPTER 2

Follow In His Footsteps

1 Peter 2:21 says that Christ left us an example so we can follow in his footsteps. In this chapter, you will discover what example God set in the very beginning. Then you will jump to the New Testament to find out what it means to follow in Christ's footsteps, and to answer these questions:

- Did Jesus practice self care?
- If so, what did he do?
- What did he tell his disciples to do?
- What did he say to a woman who was busy trying to take care of "all the things" for everyone else?

Chapter 2
Day 1

*See coloring page on page 37

Genesis 2:2-3

Observations

What did God do on the seventh day?

_____

_____

Look up the meaning of the word "rested"?

_____

_____

_____

Is it the same as being lazy? Why or why not? (Look up the definition of lazy.)

_____

_____

_____

_____

Why do you think God rested?

_____

_____

Why did God bless the seventh day to make it holy?

_____

_____

_____

Look up the meaning of the word "holy".

_____

_____

_____

_____

Ask Jesus

What else do you want me to know about this?

My Response

Mark 1:35-37

Observations

What did Jesus do first?

When did he go?

Where did he go?

What did he do when he got there?

In verse 37, what did the disciples tell Jesus?

Do you think it was selfish of Jesus to go off by himself when so many people were needing him? Why or Why not?

Do you ever feel like "everyone is looking for you?"

Ask Jesus

Is is selfish of me to go off by myself sometimes, even when I know others are needing me?

My Response

*See coloring page on page 37

Luke 5:16

Observations

What 2 things does this verse say Jesus did?

_____

How often did he do it? (Read several different Bible translations)

_____

How often do you do what Jesus did in this verse?

_____

Read a few verses before and after verse 16. Then answer the following:

Were lots of people needing/wanting something from Jesus?

_____

Does it say in these verses that Jesus only did these 2 things after everyone else's needs were met?

_____
_____
_____
_____
_____
_____
_____

Ask Jesus

Why did you do these 2 things?
Why did you not just do one or the other?

My Response

Mark 6:31-32

Observations

What did Jesus tell the disciples to do?

_____

Is what he told them to do something Jesus had ever

done before?

_____

What had the disciples been doing before Jesus told

them this?

_____

_____

_____

When Jesus told them to do this, was it because all the

people's needs were already met?

_____

_____

Why do you think Jesus told them to do that?

_____

_____

_____

_____

_____

_____

_____

_____

_____

Ask Jesus

Do you want me to also do that?
Why or why not?

My Response

Chapter 2
Day 5

*See coloring bookmark/
template on page 91

Matthew 6:25-26

Observations

What does Jesus tell us not to do/be?

_____

_____

Why is there no need for us to do/be that?

_____

_____

_____

Is it because we don't NEED food and clothing?

_____

_____

Does God know what we need?

Does God want to provide us what we need?

_____

_____

_____

What does verse 26 say you are more valuable than?

_____

Why do you think God wants to take care of birds?

_____

_____

Why are they valuable to him?

_____

_____

_____

Why do you think you are more valuable to God than

birds?

_____

_____

Ask Jesus

What is it that makes me feel like
I'm not valuable?

My Response

Luke 10:38-42

_____

_____

_____

_____

_____

_____

_____

_____

_____

_____

_____

_____

_____

Observations

Who welcomed Jesus into her house?

Who sat at Jesus' feet and listened to his teaching?

Who was "distracted" in verse 40?

In verse 41, what did Jesus tell Martha that she was?

(Notice that Jesus used different words than those in verse 40.)

In verse 40, what did Martha say that Mary was doing?

(Read several different Bible translations)

Did Jesus agree with Martha?

Did he shame Mary for not helping her sister to serve?

Do you resonate more with Mary or with Martha?

Why?

What is the ONE THING Jesus said is necessary?

Ask Jesus

What am I allowing to distract me?

My Response

On the seventh day

GOD rested from all his work

Gen. 2:2

But he withdrew HIMSELF in the deserts, and prayed.

– Luke 5:16 ASV

CHAPTER 3

Caring for Your Body

Our culture and the media give mixed messages concerning our bodies. This chapter will help you take a look at God's perspective of your body and what role your body plays in your overall life.. You will also discover commands and exhortations given in the Bible concerning how to treat your body, why it matters to God, how you can use your body to glorify God, and more.

Chapter 3
Day 1

*See coloring page on page 55

Psalm 139:13-16

Observations

How do you feel after reading & writing these verses?

_____

_____

_____

_____

Take some time now to thank and praise God for how
wonderful he made you..

_____

_____

_____

_____

_____

_____

_____

_____

_____

_____

_____

_____

Ask Jesus

What do you love about my body?

My Response

Chapter 3
Day 2

*See coloring bookmark/
template on page 91

1 Corinthians 6:19-20

Observations

What does verse 19 say your body is?

_____

_____

Does your body belong to you?

_____

Why/Why not?

_____

_____

_____

_____

How does verse 20 instruct us to glorify God?

_____

_____

What does glorify mean?

_____

_____

_____

_____

_____

_____

_____

_____

_____

_____

Ask Jesus

How can I honor you with MY body
and bring you glory?

My Response

1 Timothy 4:7-8

Observations

According to verse 8, does bodily training have any

value?

Do these verses infer that we should NOT train our bodies

at all?

How are you currently training your body?

Are you pleased with how I am
training/treating my body?
Why or why not?

My Response

Chapter 3
Day 4

Proverbs 31:17

_____

_____

_____

_____

_____

_____

_____

_____

_____

_____

_____

_____

Observations

Who makes the woman in this verse strong?

_____

_____

Why does she need to be strong?

_____

_____

_____

Why do you need to be strong?

_____

_____

_____

_____

What are you doing to make yourself strong?

_____

_____

_____

_____

_____

_____

_____

_____

Ask Jesus

What is keeping me from
becoming stronger?

My Response

1 Corinthians   10:31

Observations

How does this verse instruct us to eat and drink?

_____

How do you normally/habitually eat and drink?

_____

_____

How are your eating and drinking habits are bringing

glory to God?

_____

_____

_____

_____

_____

_____

_____

_____

_____

_____

_____

_____

_____

_____

Ask Jesus

How can I eat & drink to the
glory of God today?

My Response

Romans 12:1

_____
_____
_____
_____
_____
_____
_____
_____
_____
_____
_____
_____

Observations

In this verse what does Paul exhort us to do with our

bodies? _____

_____

Why? _____

_____

_____

What are we doing when we do this? _____

_____

_____

What does "holy" mean in this verse? _____

_____

_____

_____

Are you doing what Romans 12:1 says to do?

Why or why not? _____

_____

_____

_____

_____

_____

_____

_____

_____

Ask Jesus

What are some specific ways that I can do this today and/or this month?

My Response

I am
ENOUGH

...for I am
fearfully
—and—
wonderfully
made. -Ps. 139:14

CHAPTER 4

Caring for Your Mind

Mental health is a huge issue in our current culture. Its effects on our society can no longer be ignored. What is God's perspective of mental health, and what role do you play, if any, in the condition of your own mind? Are you powerless to change mental health disorders that have been prevalent throughout many generations? Is it possible to be transformed by changing the way you think? This chapter will help you discover what the Bible teaches about this, and uncover any ways you might be sabotaging yourself.

2 Timothy 1:7

Observations

What kind of mind does this verse God has given us?

(Hint: Read in KJV or NKJV)

_____

What word do other Bible versions use to describe this

kind of mind?

_____

_____

What else does this verse say God has given us?

_____

_____

What does this verse say God has not given us?

_____

_____

_____

_____

_____

_____

_____

_____

_____

Ask Jesus

What fear is making me believe I am powerless, unloving, stupid, crazy or un-disciplined?

My Response

Chapter 4
Day 2

*See coloring bookmark/
template on page 93

Philippians 4:8

Observations

What is the verb (action word) in this verse?

_____

What does that word mean? (Note: In the Greek, that verb is

"present" tense, which means the action is done continuously or habitually.)

_____

_____

_____

_____

Do you do that continuously or habitually?

Why or why not?

_____

_____

_____

_____

_____

_____

_____

_____

_____

Ask Jesus

What are some ideas on how I can create that as a habit?

My Response

*See coloring page on page 71

Romans 12:2

_____

_____

_____

_____

_____

_____

_____

_____

_____

_____

_____

Observations

What does this verse say NOT to do?

_____

_____

What does it say to do instead?

_____

_____

How can we be transformed?

_____

_____

_____

_____

_____

What will happen after you do what is needed to be

transformed?

_____

_____

_____

_____

_____

_____

_____

_____

_____

Ask Jesus

In what area do I need to renew my mind today?

My Response

Psalm 119:15

_____
_____
_____
_____
_____
_____
_____
_____
_____
_____
_____
_____

Observations

What does the Psalmist say he will meditate on (study, ponder) and consider (reflect on, pay close attention to, thoughtfully regard)?

_____

_____

_____

How often do you take time to do that?

_____

_____

What are some creative ways you can do that?

_____

_____

_____

_____

_____

_____

_____

_____

_____

_____

_____

Ask Jesus

What precept would it be good for me to meditate on today?

My Response

Colossians 3:2

Observations

What does this verse instruct us to set our minds on

(focus on, think about, fix our thoughts on)?

_____

_____

What does it say NOT to set our minds on?

_____

_____

Make a list of "things above":

_____

_____

_____

_____

_____

Make a list of "things on the earth"

_____

_____

_____

_____

Which things do you tend to think about most often:

_____

_____

Ask Jesus

What would be a good thing for me
to focus my thoughs on today?

My Response

1 Peter 1:13

Observations

What does this verse instruct us to do with our minds?

_____

_____

_____

What are some practical ways you can do that?

_____

_____

_____

_____

_____

_____

_____

_____

_____

_____

_____

_____

_____

_____

_____

_____

Ask Jesus

What is keeping my mind from
being alert and ready for action?

My Response

be transformed

by the **renewing**
of your mind

Romans 12:2

CHAPTER 5

Caring for Your Heart

Psalm 4:23 instructs us to "Keep your heart with all diligence, for out of it is the wellspring of life." Your heart, your soul... it is the essence of who you are, and includes your desires, intentions, and emotions. It is impossible to be completely whole and healthy if your heart and soul are not well. This chapter will help you discover what Jesus has done and continues to do to care for your heart, and what part you play in caring for your own heart.

Psalm 23: 1-3

Observations

What does David say in verse 2 that the LORD does for him?

_____

_____

In light of this, do you think it is God's will for you to rest and be refreshed?

Why or why not?

_____

In verse 3, what does David say that the LORD does to his soul?

Why do you think David wrote verse 3 after verse 2 and not the other way around?

_____

_____

_____

_____

_____

_____

_____

_____

_____

_____

Ask Jesus

In what areas of my life am I resisting your leading? Where am I trying to be the Shepherd instead of the sheep?

My Response

Chapter 5
Day 2

*See coloring page on page 87

Matthew 11:28-29

Observations

Note: I highly recommend reading these verses in the Amplified &

in the Message translations.

Who does Jesus want to come to him?

_____

Are you one of those who Jesus wants to come to him?

_____

What will he do when you come to him?

_____

What 2 things does Jesus tell us to do after we come to

him?

_____

_____

What will we find rest for?

Can our bodies truly rest if our souls are not at rest?

Why or why not?

_____

_____

_____

_____

_____

_____

_____

_____

_____

Ask Jesus

What yoke do I need to lay down today
so I can put on your yoke?

My Response

Isaiah 53:4-5

Observations

What has Jesus borne and carried?

_____

_____

_____

What was he wounded, pierced, bruised, beaten and

punished for?

_____

_____

_____

_____

Based on these Scriptures, is it God's will to heal you

from your griefs, sorrows, and emotional disorders?

Why or why not?

_____

_____

_____

_____

_____

_____

_____

_____

Ask Jesus

What else do you want me to know
about this?

My Response

Psalm 1:1-3

Observations

According to this Psalm, what does the person who is

blessed/happy not do?

1. _____

2. _____

3. _____

Do you ever do those things?

What does the person who is blessed do instead?

1. _____

2. _____

How often do you do those things?

_____

What shall this blessed person be like?

_____

_____

_____

_____

_____

_____

_____

_____

_____

_____

Ask Jesus

What Scripture do I need to
meditate on today?

My Response

Chapter 5
Day 5

*See coloring bookmark/
template on page 93

Philippians 4:11-13

Observations

Who wrote Philippians?

_____

_____

Which best describes his emotion in these verses?

Frustrated, discouraged, anxious, depressed, angry, feeling

sorry for himself, or content?

_____

_____

Was Paul only content when he had plenty?

_____

_____

How did Paul become content?

A - God performed a miracle

B - He learned how to be

_____

Why do you think Paul wrote verse 13 after verse 12 and

not before it?

_____

_____

_____

_____

Do you think Christ can give you strength to learn how to

be content in any and every situation?

_____

_____

_____

_____

_____

Ask Jesus

In what situation do I need to
receive your strength so I can
learn to be content?

My Response

Psalm 34:1-5

Observations

When does David say he will bless the LORD?

When do you bless the LORD?

In verse 4, what did the LORD do after David prayed
(sought the LORD)?

What did the LORD deliver David from?

Why do you think David did not say that God delivered
him from his enemies, or his circumstances, or from his
poverty, or from sickness?

According to verse 5, how can we be radiant with joy,
with no shame?

Ask Jesus

Let me see the expression on your
face when I look to you!

My Response

Come to me...
Learn the
unforced
rhythms of grace

Matthew 11:28-30 MSG

rest	LORD	CHRIST
rest	LORD	CHRIST
rest	Lord	Christ
come	LORD	Christ
come	LORD	GOD
come	Jesus	GOD
soul	JESUS	god
soul	Jesus	God
soul	JESUS	GOD
whatever	JESUS	GOD
whatever		
whatever		

Self-Care Scripture Bookmarks / Bible Journaling Templates

Original artwork by JoDitt Williams © 2021 JoDitt Designs For personal use and ministry use only!
----->>> Free printables at **joditt.com/joy**

Share your completed projects on social media using #JoDittDesigns and #delightintheword
Tag @JoDittWilliams on facebook and @jodittw on instagram.

ONE thing is NEEDED

Luke 10:42

When I Look to God, I am Radiant with JOY.

See Psalm 34:4-6

My body is the TEMPLE of the HOLY SPIRIT. I will HONOR GOD with my body.

See 1 Corinthians 6:19-20

God Cares for Me. So I will care for me too.

1 Peter 5:7 & Matthew 6:26

Philippians Scripture Bookmarks / Bible Journaling Templates

Original artwork by JoDitt Williams © 2021 JoDitt Designs For personal use and ministry use only!
------>>> Free printables at joditt.com/joy

Share your completed projects on social media using #JoDittDesigns and #delightintheword
Tag @JoDittWilliams on facebook and @joditw on instagram.

I will keep my thoughts **fixed** on whatever is good, pure, lovely & worthy of praise.

See Philippians 4:6-8

I can do ALL things THROUGH CHRIST which STRENGTHENS me

PHILIPPIANS 4:13

I have LEARNED the Secret of BEING CONTENT in any & EVERY Situation PHILIPPIANS 4:12

I have learned ... for ... in WHATEVER Situation I am to be CONTENT
– Phil. 4:11 ESV

ABOUT THE AUTHOR/ILLUSTRATOR

JoDitt Williams is the owner/founder of JoDitt Designs. She is an Amazon Bestselling author, artist, speaker, entrepreneur, and host of the Delight in the Word Monthly Challenges.

JoDitt is passionate about helping women use the power of pretty and creativity to delight in the written Word of God and connect with the living Word of God, so they can easily move from striving to thriving.

JoDitt equips women to accelerate their own spiritual growth and transformation while effortlessly renewing their minds and joyfully nurturing their souls... through her encouraging, inspirational blog, her private Facebook group, her delightful books, journals, art, online courses, live workshops, custom gift shop and more.

JoDitt and her husband of over 30 years live in the great state of Texas, where they love spending time with their 2 married children and 3 grandchildren.

Join JoDitt's Delight in the Word community at:
joditt.com/ditw-comm

Other Books by JoDitt:
(Available at joditt.com and on Amazon.com)

Delight in the Word of God Volume 1: Favorite Scriptures
- A Devotional Coloring Book & Journal for Adults & Teens

Delight in the Word of God Volume 2: Christmas Joy

**Lamb of God Bible Study About Jesus & Scripture Writing Journal
for Christian Women**
- A 5 Week Bible Reading Plan & Prayer Journal Notebook

SOAP Bible Study Journals & More

LEARN MORE AT joditt.com/ditwbooks

Made in the USA
Middletown, DE
19 August 2023

36978317R00057